THE EARTH FROM THE AIR

Yann Arthus-Bertrand

By photographing *The Earth from the Air* day after day, I intend to show that, now more than ever, levels and modes of consumption and exploitation of natural resources are not sustainable in the long term. Whereas world production of goods and services has multiplied by 7 since 1950, half of the world's population still lives in poverty, 20% has no access to drinking water, 40% has no sanitary facilities, and 842 million people are underfed. Our present development trends prove inadequate in relation to the stakes at hand: roughly a quarter of the land available for human use is being degraded, whole species are becoming extinct, oceans are being depleted, less and less fresh water is available, and our ever-increasing demand for energy generates greenhouse gases which, if we do not change our ways, will cause a climate change with unforeseen consequences.

At this critical stage, the alternative offered by a sustainable development policy should help in bringing about the necessary changes in order to "meet the needs of the present without compromising the ability of future generations to meet their own needs."* Inseparable from the accompanying text commentaries, *The Earth from the Air* images invite each one of us to reflect upon the planet's evolution and the future of its inhabitants.

We can and must act individually on a daily basis for the future of our children.

Yann Arthus-Bertrand

* Quoted from the Brundtland report, The world commission on environment and development : Our common future, Oxford University Press 1987.

THE EARTH FROM THE AIR

YANN ARTHUS-BERTRAND

Formation of the sea ice in the Turkü archipelago, Finland (60°27' N, 22°00' E)

Like a broken mirror, the thin ice of the Baltic breaks into sharp fragments that reflect the feeble light of a Finnish winter. This fragile sheet breaks only to reform more solidly. Sea ice floats on the current and can break up, but the fragments then meet again and pile together, until they reach their maximum thickness (an average of 20 to 25 inches, or 50 to 65 centimeters) in early April. The ice then disappears rapidly in spring, leaving the islands of the Turkü archipelago ice-free. Finland has no permanent ice sheet. Although the country is at the same latitude as Alaska and Greenland, it has a relatively temperate climate thanks to the Gulf Stream. This great warm sea current, which crosses the Atlantic and warms western Europe, may disappear as the climate changes and the Arctic ice cap melts. If this came about, Europe's climate would resemble that of Canada, which is at the same latitude.

Photo © Yann Arthus-Bertrand - www.yannarthusbertrand.org - Production : www.amiimages.com
Printed with mineral oil free ink on elementary chlorine free paper

THE EARTH FROM THE AIR

YANN ARTHUS-BERTRAND

Waste from the copper mine at Chuquicamata, Chile (22°19' S, 68°56' W)

This giant scallop shell is made of earth. A crane deposits the earth in successive, slightly curved lines giving the appearance of sheets of sand lined up side by side. The earth is extracted with the copper, but it is separated from the ore by sieving. The metal is refined in the Chuquicamata foundry that, thanks to newly installed equipment, can now filter out 95 percent of the sulfur dioxide (SO_2) and 97 percent of the arsenic that the process releases. A 1992 law aimed at reducing air pollution has required Codelco-Chile, the state-owned company that runs the mine and its facilities, to invest tens of millions of pounds to modernize them. This has not, however, prevented the company from increasing production capacity; indeed, starting in 2004, the Chuquicamata mine will have ramped up to produce 750,000 metric tons of copper per year, compared with 630,000 metric tons in 2001.

Photo © Yann Arthus-Bertrand - www.yannarthusbertrand.org - Production : www.amiimages.com
Printed with mineral oil free ink on elementary chlorine free paper

THE EARTH FROM THE AIR

YANN ARTHUS-BERTRAND

Olive harvest near Les Baux-de-Provence, Côte d'Azur, France (43°44' N, 4°47' E)

From November to February, the Mediterranean's olive harvest is in full swing. Careful harvesting provides work, protects soil from compaction by heavy machinery, and produces extremely high quality oil. Olive oil is popular all over the world for its nutritional and culinary properties, and it plays a part in many cuisines. Consumption has risen by 50 percent since 1990, rising from 1.6 million tons to 2.4 million in 1999. With its 840 million olive trees, olive cultivation in the Mediterranean has a bright future. Non-irrigated olive cultivation - which gets the best out of dry soils in a region where managing fresh water supplies is crucially important and soil degradation is a considerable problem - is an example of sustainable use of soil, preservation of landscape, and support of populations living in economically marginal rural areas. It should retain its role in a region where tourism is devouring space and increasing pressure on the land. The Mediterranean receives 30 percent of the world's tourists.

Photo © Yann Arthus-Bertrand - www.yannarthusbertrand.org - Production : www.amiimages.com
Printed with mineral oil free ink on elementary chlorine free paper

THE EARTH FROM THE AIR

YANN ARTHUS-BERTRAND

Scheggino, province of Perugia, Umbria, Italy (42°43' N, 12°50' E)

Umbria, the "green heart of Italy," is the sole region on the peninsula that has no seacoast. A world away from the beaches, its hills - dotted with fortified villages - form a gentle landscape with a medieval appearance, celebrated for its historic towns rich in art (including Assisi, Perugia, and Orvieto). Scheggino, perched at an altitude of 1,203 feet (367 m) to the east of Spoleto, stands guard over the valley of the River Nera. Beneath its tower, the village's old center huddles behind its twelfth-century walls around the church of San Niccolò (thirteenth century). All over Europe, villages cluster around their church towers, and wayside crucifixes stand at crossroads. Though secular, Europe bears the stamp of Christianity, which once was the driving force behind strife and conquest. Scheggino is famous for its delicacies, such as trout and crayfish caught in its clear streams, as well as its prized truffles. The Urbani company, which accounts for 80 percent of Italy's truffle cultivation and 40 percent of the world's production, is based in the district.

Photo © Yann Arthus-Bertrand - www.yannarthusbertrand.org - Production : www.amiimages.com
Printed with mineral oil free ink on elementary chlorine free paper

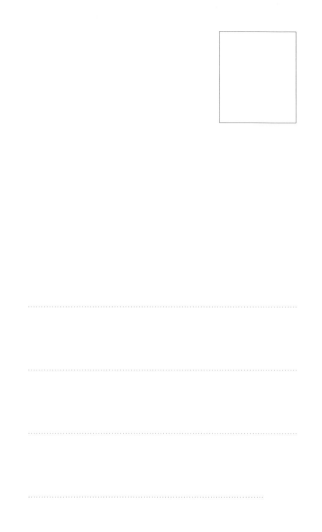

THE EARTH FROM THE AIR

YANN ARTHUS-BERTRAND

Salt drying on the coast of Quemaro, Jalisco, Mexico (19°63' N, 105°18' W)

Present in sea water in the ratio of 30 grams per liter, and in rock salt deposits of marine origin, salt is widespread throughout the planet and easily obtained either by mining or by evaporation in the sun. Only 20 percent of the world's production of 200 million metric tons is traded internationally. The United States produces 20 percent of the world's salt, and China 15 percent. Mexico, the seventh biggest producer, extracts 8 million metric tons of salt annually, exporting it to Japan and North America. Although Mexico's salt industry, on the country's Pacific coast, is highly mechanized, a few small-scale operations survive where the crystals are gathered by hand, as here. The chemical industry mops up 60 percent of the salt consumed in the world each year, and a further 10 percent is spread on icy roads. The remainder supplies the fishing industry (which uses it to preserve fish), the food industry, and is used as table salt. On average, each individual eats 7 to 8 grams of salt per day. Too much salt is unhealthy and increases the risk of developing high blood pressure. Industrially produced food contains high levels of salt, with the result that the American population consumes too much: more than 4,000 milligrams per day, almost twice the recommended daily allowance.

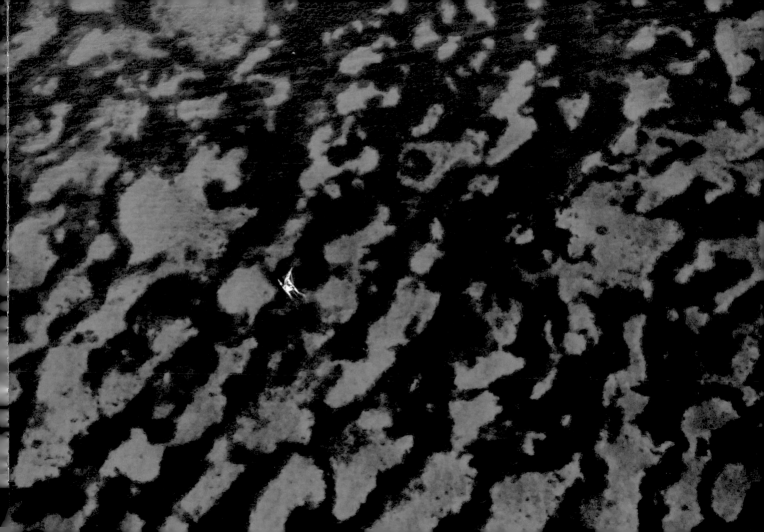

THE EARTH FROM THE AIR

YANN ARTHUS-BERTRAND

Catamaran in the Glénan archipelago, south coast of Finistère, France (47°44' N, 4°00' W)

South of the tip of Brittany's peninsula, some 9 miles (15 km) off Concarneau, the five Glénan islands and their retinue of islets and rocks cluster together on a shallow seabed of pale granite, white sand, and marl, bathed by the Atlantic. This wildly beautiful place with its clear waters, no deeper than 6.5 feet (2 m) at low tide, attracts many yachts. It is also home to France's most famous sailing school, Les Glénans, founded in 1947, and its parade of trainees in summer. But its most distinguished inhabitant is the Glénan narcissus, which grows on the archipelago and nowhere else. However, the white corollas of this flower were almost decimated by the abundant gulls, thorn bushes, and ferns. The nature reserve on the island of Saint Nicolas was set up in 1974 to ensure the species' survival, and led to an increase in the number of flowering stems from 6,500 in 1985 to 120,000 in 1998. The fragile nature of the area also demands measures to minimize the impact of humans, such as ecological sanitation, gathering rainwater, keeping to footpaths, and installing solar panels and a wind turbine for local production of nonpolluting electricity.

Photo © Yann Arthus-Bertrand · www.yannarthusbertrand.org · Production : www.amiimages.com
Printed with mineral oil free ink on elementary chlorine free paper

THE EARTH FROM THE AIR
YANN ARTHUS-BERTRAND

A glacier near Mount It-Tish, Ysyk-Köl area, Kyrgystan (78°10' E, 41°90' N)

Glaciers in Kyrgystan are so numerous (about 3,000 of them) and cover so much space (6,500 km^2) that some of them remain nameless. Their slow descent forms the valleys of the Tien-Shan mountain range, second only to the Himalayas for its numerous peaks. The highest one, Pobedy Peak, is 7,439 m high. At the heart of Central Asia, surrounded by Uzbekistan, Tadzhikistan, Kazakhstan, the Kyrgys territory is thus perched at an average height of over 3,000 m. High mountains cover close to 95% of the area, leaving very little space for sedentary agriculture. In fact, the whole country remains attached to its nomadic tradition, which is still very much alive today.

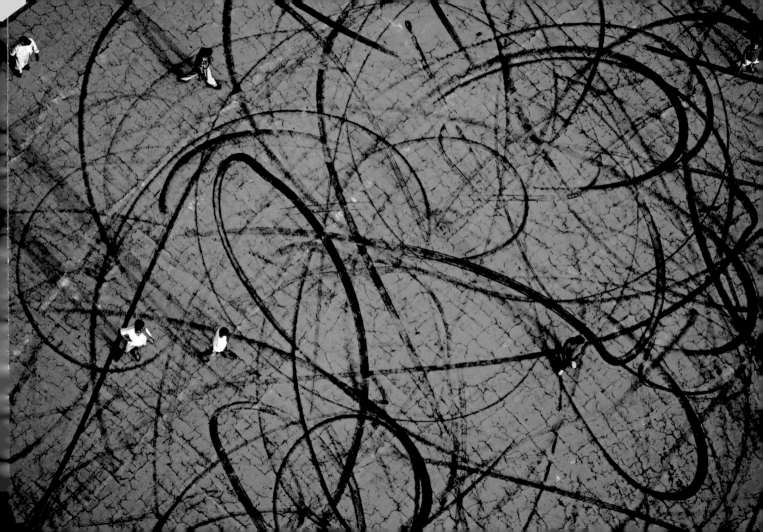

THE EARTH FROM THE AIR

YANN ARTHUS-BERTRAND

Tyre tracks on a sports ground near Doha, Qatar (25° 17' N, 51° 32' E)

Outside of Doha, capital city of Qatar, the tyres of motorcycle enthusiasts have left these surprising arabesques on the surface of a sports ground where adolescents come and meet. Qatar is a young country, with half of its inhabitants aged under 31, and a quarter under 15 - future spectators all who will applaud the Asian Games, the ASIAD scheduled in Doha for 2006. Qatar is thus the second country in the middle East to organise the Asian Games, thirty-two years after Iran, host to ASIAD in 1974. To prepare for the event, the government has launched a wide scale construction program to build sports facilities around the capital city. New stadiums, multipurpose gymnasiums for indoor sports, a cycling stadium and other equipment will offer more space for young Qatari to explore their interest in sports.

Photo © Yann Arthus-Bertrand - www.yannarthusbertrand.org - Production : www.amiimages.com
Printed with mineral oil free ink on elementary chlorine free paper

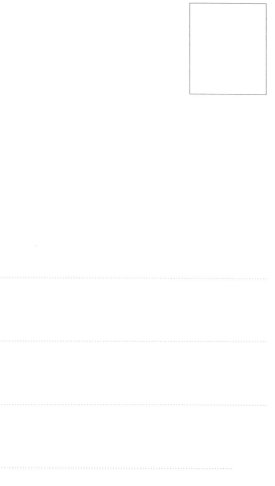

THE EARTH FROM THE AIR
YANN ARTHUS-BERTRAND

Birds flying over the lagoon near the mangroves of San Blas, Nayarit state, Mexico (21°60' N, 105°30' W)

Mexico contains a great diversity of climates and landscapes, including deserts, mountains, hardwood forests, and, as here, lagoons alongside mangroves – a subtropical rainforest typical of alluvial coasts. Although Mexico boasts more than 900 species of cactus, 1,000 orchids, and a comparable number of mammals, it is the country's variety of birds that is most striking: there are no fewer than 10,000 species, including the celebrated quetzal, also known as the "bird of the Aztecs." Mangrove swamps are a favourite haunt of migrating birds. Here they find plentiful food: insects, mollusks, shellfish, shrimp, and small fish, which come to breed at the feet of the mangroves, a tree peculiar to this mixed ecosystem that is part sea and part land. Mangroves are essential to marine life, and they also protect the shoreline, holding in place the sediments deposited by rivers and curbing the ocean's erosion by acting as a breakwater.

THE EARTH FROM THE AIR

YANN ARTHUS-BERTRAND

Trees amid the waters near Taponas, Rhône, France (46°07' N, 04°45' W)

In Taponas, in the Rhône region between the hills of Beaujolais and the hundreds of ponds scattered among the swampy Dombes area, the Saône River overflowed from March 20 - 23, 2001. This is a recurring natural phenomenon in the low-lying zone, which is downhill from the confluence of the Saône and the Doubs Rivers. Several areas in eastern and central France were submerged in the spring of 2001 as a result of flooding caused by torrential rains that fell on a ground already gorged with water and on underground water tables saturated by recent rains. However, the capricious climate was not entirely responsible. Human action also played its part with construction in flood-prone areas, obstacles to water drainage (urban and transport infrastructure), poor maintenance of rivers, and deforestation.

Photo © Yann Arthus-Bertrand - www.yannarthusbertrand.org - Production : www.amiimages.com
Printed with mineral oil free ink on elementary chlorine free paper

THE EARTH FROM THE AIR
YANN ARTHUS-BERTRAND

Buccaneer Archipelago, West Kimberley, Australia (16°17' S, 123°20' E)

Thousands of uncultivated islands, including Buccaneer Archipelago, emerge from the waters off the jagged, eroded coasts of northwestern Australia. Because there is scant agricultural or industrial activity on the shoreline, the waters of the Timor Sea that surround these islands have remained relatively untouched by pollution. This has allowed fragile species such as the Pinctada maxima oyster to develop. Harvested in their natural setting of the sea floor, these mollusks are exploited for the production of cultured pearls. Australian pearls, which make up 70 percent of those produced in the South Seas, are twice as large (averaging a half-inch, or 12 mm, in diameter) as those of Japan and, according to experts, finer in appearance. Japan pioneered the pearl industry at the turn of the twentieth century and is the world's leading producer.

THE EARTH FROM THE AIR
YANN ARTHUS-BERTRAND

Dairy cows passing between dunes, Maule province, Chile (35°16' S, 73°20' W)

The wind sweeps the volcanic dust before it. Here, an oceanic climate showers the land with abundant moisture, allowing grass to grow rapidly, thereby making in favourable for livestock farming. The country is known for its "crazy geography": it measures 2,608 miles (4,200 km) from north to south, stretching over 35 degrees of latitude, but is only 62 miles wide at its narrowest point, and 250 miles at its widest (100 and 450 km). This means that the north is extremely arid; the Chilean economy here is dominated by copper, iron ore, and sulphur mining. The center has a more Mediterranean climate and contains the biggest cities and associated industry, as well as farming - chiefly fruit and vineyards. In the south, with its oceanic climate, fields give way to pasture, vast forests, and lakes until, gradually, the great glaciers of Patagonia take over. Chile finally comes to an end at the far southern tip of South America, not far from the Antarctic circle.

THE EARTH FROM THE AIR

YANN ARTHUS-BERTRAND

Countryside around Siena, Tuscany, Italy (43°19' N, 11°19' E)

Washed by the Tyrrhenian Sea, Tuscany in central Italy is one of the loveliest regions of the entire peninsula. Tuscany owes part of its fame to its hills, covered with vineyards, olive trees, corn and barley fields, and punctuated with medieval villages. Tuscans developed "ecotourism" at an early date. Local enterprises, especially artisans, now adhere to Social Accountability 8000 (SA 8000), an international standard based on the principles of human rights delineated in International Labour Organization Conventions, the U.N. Convention on the Rights of the Child, and the Universal Declaration of Human Rights. SA 8000 is a voluntary standard that ensures that economic development occurs through the ethical sourcing of goods and services.

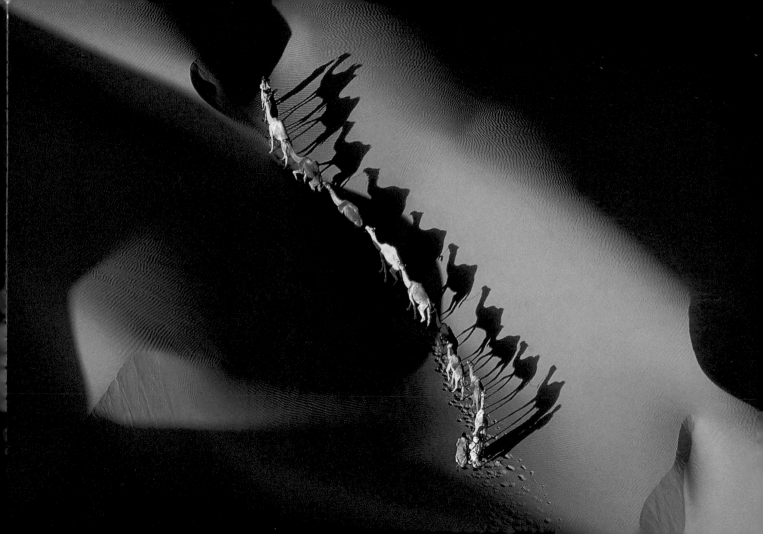

THE EARTH FROM THE AIR

YANN ARTHUS-BERTRAND

Dromedary caravans near Nouakchott, Mauritania (18°09' N, 15°29' W)

The dromedary, perfectly adapted to the aridity, is an important national livestock in Mauritania and all of the other countries bordering the Sahara. Its domestication several thousand years ago enabled humans to conquer the desert and develop trans-saharan trade routes. The dromedary eats 25 to 50 pounds (10 to 12 kg) of vegetables a day and can survive without water for many months in the winter. In the summer, because of the heat and expended effort, the dromedary can last only a few days without drinking; by comparison, a human would die of dehydration within twenty-four hours. The reserve fat contained in its single hump helps in thermal regulation, allowing the dromedary to withstand the heating of its body without needing to perspire to cool down. The Maurs, the ethnic majority in Mauritania, raise the dromedary for its milk and meat as well as its skin and wool. In 2001 the country's dromedary livestock numbered about 1 million.

Photo © Yann Arthus-Bertrand · www.yannarthusbertrand.org · Production : www.amiimages.com
Printed with mineral oil free ink on elementary chlorine free paper

THE EARTH FROM THE AIR
YANN ARTHUS-BERTRAND

Lakagigar Volcano Chain, Iceland (64°04' N, 18°15' W)

Lakagigar, in southern Iceland, still bears the scars of one of the most violent volcanic eruptions in recorded history. In 1783 two eruptive fissures, a total of 15 miles (25 km) long, opened up on both sides of Laki volcano, vomiting 4 cubic miles (15 km^3) of molten rock that engulfed 225 square miles (580 km^2) of land, the largest lava flow in human memory. A cloud of carbon dioxide, sulfur dioxide, and ash spread over the entire island and contaminated grazing land and surface waters. Three quarters of the livestock was annihilated, and after a second eruption in 1785, a terrible famine decimated a quarter of the population (more than 10,000 people). The fissures of Lakagigar, crowned by 115 volcanic craters, are today closed up, and the streams of lava are covered by a thick carpet of moss. Iceland has more than 200 active volcanoes and has produced one-third of all discharges of lava occurring around the world in the course of the last 500 years.

THE EARTH FROM THE AIR
YANN ARTHUS-BERTRAND

Illuminated Greenhouse near Sauvo, Varsinais-Suomi region, Finland (60°18' N, 22°36' E)

Finland occupies the most northern position in Europe, with a quarter of its territory located above the Arctic Circle. At such high latitudes agriculture faces natural challenges: in winter, night lasts uninterrupted for nearly two months in the north, while in the south the the sun does not appear for more than six hours daily. In this premature twilight the snow is scattered with gleams from greenhouses, where the daily duration of photosynthesis is extended by artificial lighting, as here near Sauvo, in the southwestern part of the country. Finland manages to thus produce 35,500 tons of tomatoes per year; but its greatest crop remains timber. It exploits pine and birch forests that cover 70 percent of its land and provide more than one-third of its export revenues. Residue from the timber industry and waste from cutting trees serve as fuel, an important source of renewable energy that covered 20 percent of the country's energy consumption and 10 percent of its electricity consumption in the year 2000.

THE EARTH FROM THE AIR

YANN ARTHUS-BERTRAND

Icebergs off the Adelie coast, South Pole (67°00' S, 139°00' E)

These drifting icebergs recently detached from the glacial platforms of Antarctica, as can be seen from their flat shape and the ice strata that are still visible on their jagged sides. Like the rest of the 480 cubic miles that detach every year from Antarctica, these icebergs will slowly be eroded by the winds and waves before disappearing. Antarctica is a place of extremes: temperatures reach as low as - 94° F (- 70 °C), and winds reach speeds of 200 miles (300 km) an hour. The continent has an area of 5,500 square miles (14 million km²) and contains 90 percent of the ice and 70 percent of the freshwater reserves of the planet. Antarctica has been governed since 1959 by the Washington Treaty, which gives it international status and restricts its uses to scientific activities. The Russian station at Vostok has extracted, from a depth of 11,800 feet (3,623 m), chunks of ice that have made possible the reconstruction of more than 420,000 years of history of the climate and atmospheric composition. The atmosphere's current content of carbon dioxide - the main gas responsible for global warming - is higher than it has been for 160,000 years.

THE EARTH FROM THE AIR

YANN ARTHUS-BERTRAND

Landscape of brightly coloured fields near Sarraud, Vaucluse, France (44°01' N, 05°24' E)

On the Vaucluse plateau, an arid limestone upland in the east of the *département*, lavender fields blossom in the Mediterranean summer heat. Cultivation of fine lavender began around 1920 when the crop was distilled to produce an essential oil for perfume. Now, however, it faces competition from lavandin and synthetic products. By 1992, annual production had dropped to 25 tons (a sixth of production totals in 1960). This decline is all the more worrying in that lavender cultivation, which makes use of arid land, supports rural communities in mountainous areas where agriculture is in decline. A program to relaunch and modernize this activity was started in 1994. In 2000, 9,884 acres (4,000 ha) produced 65 tons of essential oil (70 percent of world output), and a further 1,235 acres (500 ha) produced flowers and bouquets. The perfumed, purple carpets that are strewn over the landscapes of Haute Provence are also a considerable asset for tourism in southeast France. In less than a century, the evolution of rural life has given this little flower an important role in developing the local economy.

THE EARTH FROM THE AIR

YANN ARTHUS-BERTRAND

Market near Xochimilco district, Mexico (19°20' N, 99°05' W)

This mosaic of brightly colored parasols hides a bustling, noisy market, set up for the day in a street of the capital. Shaded from the sun, stalls selling fruit, vegetables, herbal remedies and spices sit side by side with others that sell cloth and craft artefacts. Mexico's flourishing markets are a national institution, held daily all over the country. Like their crafts, their traditional clothing, and the façades of buildings, the markets express Mexicans' love of vivid, bright colors, such as the brilliant pink known as "rosa Mexicana." Internationally, Mexico is a world champion of commercial vigour, with exports growing at the rate of 18 percent - with more than 85 percent of these going to the United States. But although economic liberalization led to a doubling in gross domestic product per capita between 1985 and 1999, it worsened inequality in the distribution of wealth. In rural areas, where agriculture cannot compete with imports, average earnings are as little as a quarter of the national average. The social unrest that has troubled the state of Chiapas since 1994 is partly due to this.

Photo © Yann Arthus-Bertrand · www.yannarthusbertrand.org · Production : www.amiimages.com
Printed with mineral oil free ink on elementary chlorine free paper

THE EARTH FROM THE AIR
YANN ARTHUS-BERTRAND

New olive plantings, Zaghouan, Tunisia (36°24' N, 10°23' E)

These olive groves at the base of the 4,250-foot-high (1,295 m) Jebel Zaghouan in northeastern Tunisia are planted in curved embankments to retain water and limit erosion, which viewed from above look like the lines on a relief map. A symbol of peace, the tree is native to the Mediterranean basin, where 90 percent of the planet's olive trees grow. An olive tree can live as long as 1,000 years, producing 11 to 65 pounds (5 to 30 kg) of olives yearly. In the past its oil was used in small clay lamps, but it has been replaced by petroleum. Today we consume both table olives and olive oil, which are renowned for their dietetic and medicinal properties and are also used in cosmetics. It take 11 to 13 pounds (5 to 6 kilograms) of olives to produce a liter (a bit more than a quart) of olive oil. Tunisia produced 1 million tons of olives in 2000, doubling its 1997 production and becoming the fourth-greatest producer, after Spain (4.2 million tons), Italy (2.8 million), and Greece (2 million). These countries are also the principal consumers of olive oil: 20 liters per capita each year in Greece, 15 liters in Spain and Italy, and just one-half liter in France.

Taking Stock

The world's population has more than doubled in the last fifty years, and a further 50 percent increase is expected by 2050.

Year	World Population (in billions)
1950	2.5
2002	6.2
2050	8 to 9[1]

If we imagine the Earth as a village with 100 inhabitants, sixty of these people live in Asia. Fourteen of them live in Africa. There are nine each in South America and Europe, five in North America, two in Russia, and one in Oceania[2].

A large proportion of the population has no access to adequate health care or education.

• 815 million people (one in seven) are malnourished[3].
• 1.1 billion people (one in six) have no access to clean drinking water[4].
• 133 million children (one child in five) do not go to school[5]; 97 percent of these children live in developing countries.
• 860 million adults (one adult in five) cannot read or write[6]; of these, 544 million are women.
• 19 percent of children aged five to fourteen go to work[7].

Rising demand for energy and a massive reliance on fossil fuels, which are not renewable, mean that these resources will not last long.

Between now and 2020, our energy use has been projected to increase at the rate of 1.5 percent per year[8].

In 2000, 79.5 percent of primary energy production came from fossil fuels[9].

Energy Source	Share of World Output
Oil	34.9 percent
Gas	21.1 percent
Coal	23.5 percent
Nuclear	6.8 percent
Other (renewable energy sources)	13.8 percent (10.7 percent of which is biomass, mainly wood)

Today, the world burns as much oil in six weeks as it burned in one year in 1950.[11]

For many, good health is out of reach.

	Least Developed Countries	Developing Countries	Industrialized Countries	Whole World
Mortality rate in children under the age of five[12]:	157	89	7	82
Risk of mother's death as a result of childbirth[13]:	1 in 16	1 in 61	1 in 4.085	1 in 75

In 2002, average life expectancy worldwide was sixty-seven. In Africa, average life expectancy was fifty-three, while in North America it was seventy seven, and eighty-one in Japan.[13].
HIV/AIDS affected 42 million people[14] in 2002. Of those, 90 percent lived in developing countries and 75 percent lived in sub-Saharan Africa[14].

A minority of the population is using up most of the world's resources.
• 20 percent of people live in developed countries.
• They consume 53 percent of the world's energy[15].
• They eat 44 percent of the world's meat[16].
• They own about 80 percent of the world's motor vehicles.

Inequality in access to clean water produces huge differences in consumption.

Country	Drinking Water Consumption per Person per Day[17]
France	255.2 quarts (290 liters)
United States	519.2 quarts (590 liters)
China	77.44 quarts (88 liters)
Mali	10.56 quarts (12 liters)

Beyond these inequalities, however, humanity faces common issues.

Human activity is enhancing the greenhouse effect, leading to climate change.
For the last 150 years, industry has been releasing carbon dioxide (CO_2) into the atmosphere at a rate millions of times greater than the rate at which it was originally accumulated underground.
If nothing is done, global temperatures could rise by up to 42.8° F (6 °C) by 2100, with economic, social, and environmental consequences.
To limit the disastrous effects of global warming, the world's CO_2 emissions would have to be cut by 50 percent; this would demand an 80-percent reduction by developed countries.

Measures must be taken to ensure that our level of energy consumption allows development in a sustainable way.

Country	Emissions of Carbon Equivalent in Kilograms per Person per Year (base 2000)	Factor by Which Present Emissions Exceed Sustainable Level (of 500 kg/person/year)
United States	6,718	13.4
Germany	3,292	6.6
France	2,545	5.1
Mexico	1,000	2
Mozambique	416	0.83 (does not exceed)

Reduction in biodiversity does not just damage the fertility of our fields—it reduces our chances of finding new medicines.
In 2002, 24 percent of mammals, 12 percent of birds, and 30 percent of fish were in danger of extinction.
Half of the world's mangrove forests, essential to the survival of 75 percent of the world's commercially exploited marine species, have disappeared.
Primary tropical forests, which are reserves for the world's biodiversity, are disappearing fast—at a rate of about 15 million hectares per year. (The nation of Ireland occupies about 7.5 million hectares, half the area of the primary tropical forests lost every year).

However, there are signs that people are becoming aware of what is happening.
Since the United Nations held the 1992 Earth Summit in Rio de Janeiro the serious risks and consequences, of the destruction of natural resources have been increasingly taken into account by politicians all over the world.
Since 1990, more than 7,000 international non-governmental organizations (NGOs) have been formed[18] with a focus on environmental and social issues. The number of international NGOs and the actions they are taking over are both growing inexorably.
The rising success of fair trade products allows everyone to take action as a consumer. An example is the Max Havelaar label, whose sales outlets grew in number from 250 to 3,500 in just three years.

There is still time to act.
Our apparent wealth is founded on economic growth, whose indicators ignore the exhaustion of natural resources. Prices take no account of environmental and social costs. For example, the price of a pound of wheat does not include the cost that the public pays to clean up the polluted water supply used to grow the crop. According to Amartya Sen, 1998 Nobel Laureate in Economics, there is now an urgent need to reassess the basic workings of the market.

The ball is in our court.
We can all take action by reducing unnecessary consumption and putting pressure on governments and industry to embrace sustainable development. Today, the choice is still ours between regulating ourselves or having regulations forced upon us. There is more room for manoeuvre if we have twenty years to implement those regulations than if we have only one week.

Maximilien Rouer

Chief Executive of BeCitizen, Maximilien Rouer, M.S., studied engineering at the national agronomy institute in Paris. BeCitizen was formed in 2000 with the mission of promoting sustainable development. In France, the company is a leader in sustainable development expertise and consultancy. BeCitizen is a member of France's national sustainable development council.

Notes
1   Total Midyear Population for the World: 1950–2050. U.S. Bureau of the Census, International Data Base (www.census.gov/ipc/www/worldpop.html).
2   World Population Data Sheet 2002. Population Reference Bureau (www.prb.org).
3   U.N. Food and Agriculture Organization–1997/1999 figures.
4   U.N. Joint Monitoring Programme, September 2002
5   Human Development Report, 2002. U.N. Development Programme (http://hdr.undp.org/reports/global/2002/en).
6   UNESCO – 2000 figures
7   UNICEF
8   Energy Information Agency (www.eia.doe.gov).
9   International Energy Agency (www.iea.org).
10 Vital Signs 2001. Worldwatch Institute (www.worldwatch.org).
11 UNICEF – 2001figures
12 UNICEF
13 2002 World Population Data Sheet, Population Reference Bureau (www.prb.org).
14 UNAIDS: Joint United Nations Programme on HIV/AIDS (www.unaids.org).
15 Human Development Report, 2002. U.N. Development Programme (http://hdr.undp.org/reports/global/2002/en).
16 Energy Statistics of OECD Countries, 1999–2000. International Energy Agency (www.iea.org).
17 Source: UN Food and Agriculture Organisation – 2002 figures http://www.fao.org/WAICENT/faoinfo/economic/giews/english/fo/fo0205/Y6668e13.htm
18 AQUASTAT: FAO's Information System on Water and Agriculture (www.fao.org).
19 UN Framework Convention on Climate Change (www.unfccc.int); for emissions figures for Mexico and Mozambique, refer to Intergovernmental Panel on Climate Change (www.ipcc.ch).
20 This is also the size of the state of Florida.
21 Human Development Report, 2002. U.N. Development Programme (http://hdr.undp.org/reports/global/2002/en).
22 Ibid.